WOULD YOU RATHER?

Gross Kids Only

Sick Scenarios for Kids Age 7

7

Year Old Edition

Try Not To Laugh Challenge®
BONUS PLAY

Join our Joke Club and get the Bonus Play PDF!

Simply send us an email to:

TNTLPublishing@gmail.com

and you will get the following:

- 10 Hilarious Would You Rather Questions
- An entry in our Monthly Giveaway of a $50 Amazon Gift card!

We draw a new winner each month and will contact you via email!

Good luck!

CRAZY COREY

Welcome to
The Try Not to Laugh Challenge®
Would You Rather?
GROSS EDITION

RULES:

• Face your opponent and decide who is
Player 1 and Player 2.

• Starting with Player 1, read the Would You Rather
question aloud and pick an answer. The same player
will then explain why they chose that answer in the
most hilarious or wacky way possible!

• If the reason makes Player 2 laugh, then a laugh
point is scored!

• Take turns going back and forth, then mark your
total laugh points at the end of each round!

• Whoever gets the most laugh points is officially
crowned the Gross Laugh Master!

• If ending with a tie, finish with the Tie-Breaker
round for WINNER TAKES ALL!

Most importantly, have fun and be SILLY!

REMEMBER, these scenarios listed in the
book are solely for fun and games!
Please do NOT attempt any of the crazy
scenarios in this book.

PLAYER 1

(DON'T FORGET TO EXPLAIN YOUR ANSWERS!)

Would you rather let a worm crawl up your nose OR let a ladybug crawl in your ear?

Laugh Point_____ /1

Would you rather eat Oreos that taste like buttered popcorn, OR eat popcorn that tastes like Oreos?

Laugh Point_____ /1

PLAYER 1

(DON'T FORGET TO EXPLAIN YOUR ANSWERS!)

Would you rather keep seven beehives under your bed OR let one hungry alligator sleep with you?

Laugh Point____ /1

Would you rather watch a volcano erupt with biscuits and gravy OR see a giant pizza asteroid hit earth?

Laugh Point____ /1

PASS THE BOOK TO PLAYER 2!

PLAYER 2

(DON'T FORGET TO EXPLAIN YOUR ANSWERS!)

Would you rather kiss a squid on the cheek OR kiss a moose on the lips?

Laugh Point_____/1

Would you rather never brush your teeth OR never cut your toenails?

Laugh Point_____/1

10

PLAYER 2

Would you rather sculpt a statue made of ear wax OR smell the armpits of everyone in your town?

Laugh Point_____ /1

Would you rather lick the entire toilet seat OR lick 1,000 envelopes?

Laugh Point_____ /1

TIME TO SCORE YOUR POINTS! →

PLAYER 1

/4

ROUND TOTAL

PLAYER 2

/4

ROUND TOTAL

ROUND WINNER

PLAYER 1

Would you rather have VERY long legs with tiny T-Rex arms, OR teeny baby legs with arms so long they touch the ground ?

Laugh Point____ /1

Would you rather try the spiciest hot sauce of all time OR try the stinkiest cheese there ever was?

Laugh Point____ /1

PLAYER 1

(DON'T FORGET TO EXPLAIN YOUR ANSWERS!)

Would you rather have glow in the dark skin **OR** have eyes that give you night vision?

Laugh Point_____ /1

Would you rather have the longest tongue **OR** the biggest ears, in the world?

Laugh Point_____ /1

PASS THE BOOK TO PLAYER 2!

PLAYER 2

Would you rather have to walk with wet socks in your shoes OR wet underwear in your pants?

Laugh Point_____ /1

Would you rather have hands that could stick to anything OR feet that had wheels on them?

Laugh Point_____ /1

PLAYER 2

(DON'T FORGET TO EXPLAIN YOUR ANSWERS!)

Would you rather have
a tongue like a lizard
OR eyes like a cat?

Laugh Point____ /1

Would you rather laugh every
time you heard something
sad OR cry every time
you heard good news?

Laugh Point____ /1

TIME TO SCORE YOUR POINTS! →

PLAYER 1

/4

ROUND TOTAL

PLAYER 2

/4

ROUND TOTAL

ROUND
WINNER

18

ROUND 3

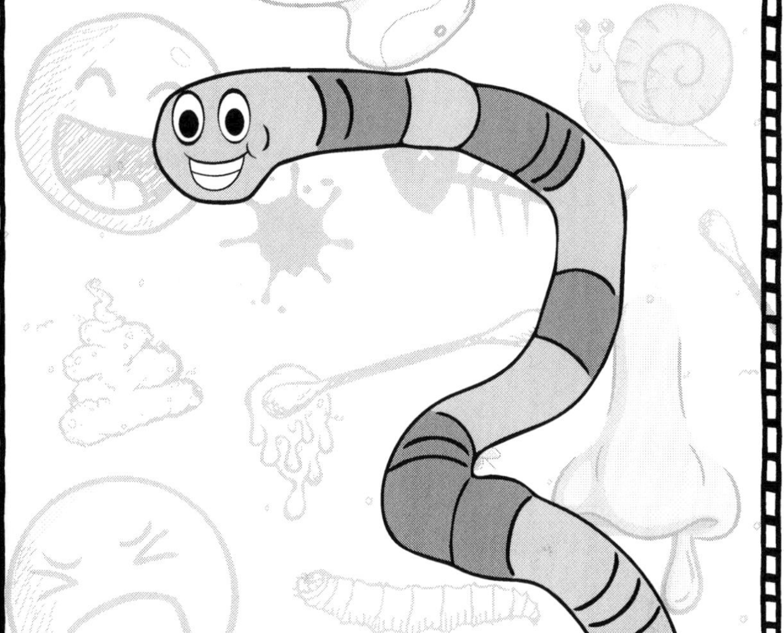

PLAYER 1

Would you rather accidentally pass bad gas on the bus, OR accidentally burp as loud as Shrek in church?

Laugh Point____ /1

Would you rather eat a portion of your pet's food OR eat a slice of pizza that fell on the floor, then sat on the counter for 24 hours?

Laugh Point____ /1

PLAYER 1

(DON'T FORGET TO EXPLAIN YOUR ANSWERS!)

Would you rather eat 10 ghost pepper pizzas OR 10 sardine burgers?

Laugh Point____ /1

Would you rather have a big nose with a green wart OR a small nose with a big booger?

Laugh Point____ /1

PASS THE BOOK TO PLAYER 2!

21

PLAYER 2

Would you rather have dinner with a wild gorilla OR share a bed with a sneaky tarantula?

Laugh Point____ /1

Would you rather be the only janitor in all of New Zealand OR the only cook in all of Rhode Island?

Laugh Point____ /1

PLAYER 2

(DON'T FORGET TO EXPLAIN YOUR ANSWERS!)

Would you rather go swimming in the freezing winter OR run laps in the hot summer heat?

Laugh Point____/1

Would you rather hold a greasy pig by its back legs OR wrestle with three irritated alligators?

Laugh Point____/1

TIME TO SCORE YOUR POINTS! →

23

PLAYER 1

/4

ROUND TOTAL

PLAYER 2

/4

ROUND TOTAL

ROUND WINNER

PLAYER 1

Would you rather take a big gulp of spoiled milk OR a big bite out of a rotten banana?

Laugh Point____/1

Would you rather eat a literal finger sandwich OR fresh brain stew?

Laugh Point____/1

PLAYER 1

Would you rather get caught lying and have your nose grow every time you lie, OR get away with lying but develop an itchy rash on your back each time you lie?

Laugh Point____/1

Would you rather have gummy worm eyebrows and lips OR have spaghetti for hair?

Laugh Point____/1

PASS THE BOOK TO PLAYER 2!

PLAYER 2

Would you rather clip an old lady's toenails OR trim an old man's nose hairs?

Laugh Point____/1

Would you rather always have sand in everything you eat OR always find hair in your meals?

Laugh Point____/1

28

PLAYER 2

(DON'T FORGET TO EXPLAIN YOUR ANSWERS!)

Would you rather wear the same socks OR the same underwear, every day?

Laugh Point_____ /1

Would you rather live forever as a grasshopper, OR live 9 lives as an unlucky cat?

Laugh Point_____ /1

TIME TO SCORE YOUR POINTS! →

PLAYER 1

/4

ROUND TOTAL

PLAYER 2

/4

ROUND TOTAL

ROUND
WINNER

ROUND

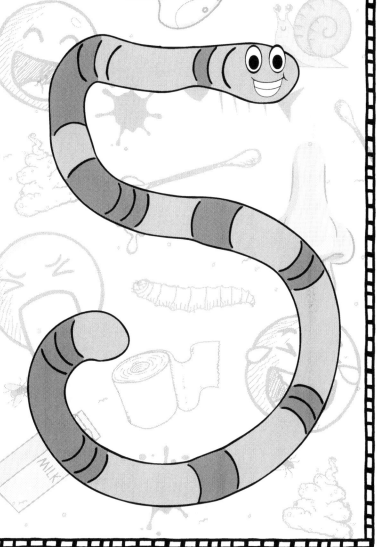

PLAYER 1

Would you rather smell your dad's dirty socks for 20 seconds straight, OR be stuck in a room with your dog who has a case of bad gas?

Laugh Point_____ /1

Would you rather drink a smoothie made out of slugs OR eat oatmeal covered in ants?

Laugh Point_____ /1

PLAYER 1

Would you rather have a pegleg made of candy OR a hook-hand made out of a giant pretzel?

Laugh Point_____ /1

Would you rather eat 20 marshmallow-stuffed tacos, OR 10 giant gummy worm burritos?

Laugh Point_____ /1

PASS THE BOOK TO PLAYER 2!

PLAYER 2

Would you rather eat a pine cone covered in peanut butter OR eat a grass salad with mud dressing?

Laugh Point_____ /1

Would you rather have every minute of your life put on YouTube OR never be able to use YouTube again?

Laugh Point_____ /1

PLAYER 2

(DON'T FORGET TO EXPLAIN YOUR ANSWERS!)

Would you rather develop permanent hiccups OR never-ending rapid eye blinking?

Laugh Point_____ /1

Would you rather wear socks made of sandpaper OR wear gloves made of tissue paper?

Laugh Point_____ /1

TIME TO SCORE YOUR POINTS! →

PLAYER 1

/4

ROUND TOTAL

PLAYER 2

/4

ROUND TOTAL

ROUND WINNER

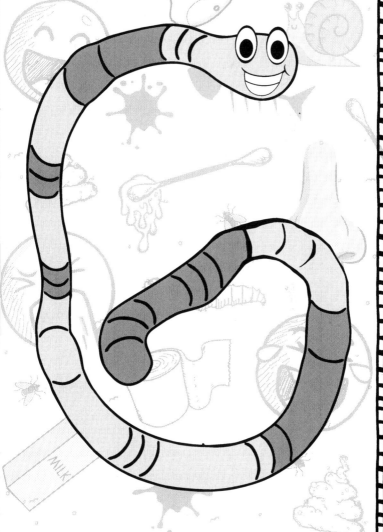

PLAYER 1

Would you rather clean up an overflowing trash dumpster filled with dog poop OR handwash 300 dirty dishes?

Laugh Point____ /1

Would you rather never wear matching shoes OR never wear matching clothes?

Laugh Point____ /1

PLAYER 1

(DON'T FORGET TO EXPLAIN YOUR ANSWERS!)

Would you rather use toothpaste made out of snail guts OR mouthwash made out of dog spit?

Laugh Point_____ /1

Would you rather have to eat a handful of sand OR eat ten ants?

Laugh Point_____ /1

PASS THE BOOK TO PLAYER 2!

PLAYER 2

Would you rather drink a sardine, sour cream, and salsa smoothie OR eat a chocolate, crab, and curry cupcake?

Laugh Point____ /1

Would you rather always have to walk on your hands OR always have to slither on your belly?

Laugh Point____ /1

PLAYER 2

(DON'T FORGET TO EXPLAIN YOUR ANSWERS!)

Would you rather see with your ears OR hear with your kneecaps?

Laugh Point____/1

Would you rather have the head of a fish OR the head of a donkey?

Laugh Point____/1

TIME TO SCORE YOUR POINTS! →

PLAYER 1

/4

ROUND TOTAL

PLAYER 2

/4

ROUND TOTAL

ROUND WINNER

ROUND

PLAYER 1

(DON'T FORGET TO EXPLAIN YOUR ANSWERS!)

Would you rather own a giant pet dragon OR a tiny pet unicorn?

Laugh Point_____ /1

Would you rather share a room with your parents OR share a room with all your siblings?

Laugh Point_____ /1

PLAYER 1

(DON'T FORGET TO EXPLAIN YOUR ANSWERS!)

Would you rather smell like onions every Friday OR have to talk with chocolate Oreos stuck in your teeth, every Monday?

Laugh Point_____ /1

Would you rather be a professional pooper scooper OR a Port-O-Potty toilet cleaner?

Laugh Point_____ /1

PASS THE BOOK TO PLAYER 2!

Would you rather be a caterpillar that turned into a butterfly OR a snail that turned into a cobra?

Laugh Point_____ /1

Would you rather be able to eat and not gain excess weight OR play sports and never need to shower?

Laugh Point_____ /1

PLAYER 2

Would you rather rake up leaves with a fork OR shovel snow with a spoon?

Laugh Point_____/1

Would you rather own a huge dog with a squeaky bark OR a tiny dog that roars like a lion?

Laugh Point_____/1

TIME TO SCORE YOUR POINTS! →

PLAYER 1

/4

ROUND TOTAL

PLAYER 2

/4

ROUND TOTAL

ROUND
WINNER

ROUND

PLAYER 1

Would you rather eat a living worm OR eat the dirt you pulled it out of?

Laugh Point_____ /1

Would you rather smush cat poop between your toes, OR eat what's between them after gym class?

Laugh Point_____ /1

PLAYER 1

Would you rather one of your fingers be fork-shaped OR one of your toes be spoon-shaped?

Laugh Point_____ /1

Would you rather have to crawl through a sewer OR get pooped on by a dinosaur?

Laugh Point_____ /1

PASS THE BOOK TO PLAYER 2!

PLAYER 2

Would you rather have a small, unfindable cricket chirping in your room all night, OR have a silent cricket in your room that's the size of a horse?

Laugh Point_____/1

Would you rather write with large Hulk hands OR talk on the phone while wearing vampire teeth?

Laugh Point_____/1

PLAYER 2

Would you rather your mom plant a big, red lipstick kiss on your forehead, OR your dad insist on making your lunch using leftover spaghetti for a sandwich?

Laugh Point_____ /1

Would you rather ride to school in a kangaroo's pouch OR a pelican's beak?

Laugh Point_____ /1

TIME TO SCORE YOUR POINTS! →

PLAYER 1

/4

ROUND TOTAL

PLAYER 2

/4

ROUND TOTAL

ROUND WINNER

ROUND

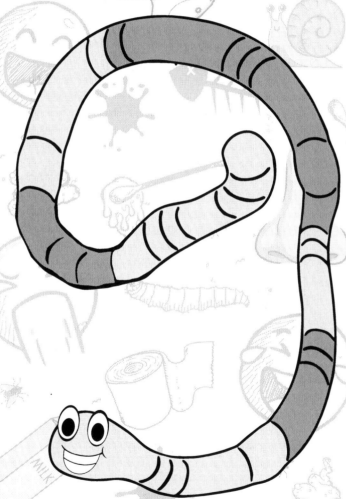

PLAYER 1

(DON'T FORGET TO EXPLAIN YOUR ANSWERS!)

Would you rather have an actual monster in your closet OR a ghost that lives under your bed?

Laugh Point____/1

Would you rather climb the world's tallest tree OR spend a day in the world's biggest igloo?

Laugh Point____/1

PLAYER 1

Would you rather get bitten by a radioactive koala bear and get super powers, OR have the power to make it rain candy anytime?

Laugh Point_____ /1

Would you rather be a giant with short arms OR be a smurf with long arms?

Laugh Point_____ /1

PASS THE BOOK TO PLAYER 2!

PLAYER 2

Would you rather have to wear a dress/suit to school every day OR shave your head to be bald?

Laugh Point____ /1

Would you rather walk barefoot across a floor covered in LEGO's, OR walk barefoot across hot coals?

Laugh Point____ /1

PLAYER 2

(DON'T FORGET TO EXPLAIN YOUR ANSWERS!)

Would you rather have to say "NO" to everything someone asked you, OR only be able to sing anytime you speak?

Laugh Point_____ /1

Would you rather have the ability to turn into a dragon OR the ability to turn other people into hamsters?

Laugh Point_____ /1

TIME TO SCORE YOUR POINTS! →

PLAYER 1

/4

ROUND TOTAL

PLAYER 2

/4

ROUND TOTAL

ROUND WINNER

ROUND

PLAYER 1

(DON'T FORGET TO EXPLAIN YOUR ANSWERS!)

Would you rather spend the night in a casket OR a giant bed of insects?

Laugh Point_____/1

Would you rather smell your own earwax OR eat one of your boogers?

Laugh Point_____/1

PLAYER 1

Would you rather clip your toenails and fingernails by biting them, OR clean your underwear by licking them?

Laugh Point_____ /1

Would you rather climb a mountain of dirty socks OR dig a tunnel through a pile of rotten meat?

Laugh Point_____ /1

PASS THE BOOK TO PLAYER 2!

PLAYER 2

Would you rather eat uncooked chicken OR drink hot carrot juice?

Laugh Point_____ /1

Would you rather sleepwalk through a cave of 1,000 bats OR through a den of three wolves?

Laugh Point_____ /1

PLAYER 2

Would you rather jump out of a hot air balloon onto a pudding mattress, OR somersault off a lighthouse and land in an ocean of sticky fudge?

Laugh Point_____/1

Would you rather be able to karate chop through a pile of bricks OR lift a train with one hand?

Laugh Point_____/1

TIME TO SCORE YOUR POINTS! →

PLAYER 1

/4
ROUND TOTAL

PLAYER 2

/4
ROUND TOTAL

ROUND WINNER

ADD UP ALL YOUR POINTS FROM EACH ROUND.
THE PLAYER WITH THE MOST POINTS IS
CROWNED
THE GROSS LAUGH MASTER!

IN THE EVENT OF A TIE, CONTINUE TO
ROUND 11 FOR THE TIE-BREAKER!

PLAYER 1 _____
GRAND TOTAL

PLAYER 2 _____
GRAND TOTAL

_____

THE GROSS
LAUGH MASTER

ROUND

TIE-BREAKER
(WINNER TAKES ALL!)

PLAYER 1

(DON'T FORGET TO EXPLAIN YOUR ANSWERS!)

Would you rather have to smash rotten eggs with your toes OR clean toilets using your bare hands?

Laugh Point_____ /1

Would you rather have to call for help from getting your shoelace caught in the escalator, OR because you got a noodle stuck up your nose?

Laugh Point_____ /1

PLAYER 1

Would you rather only be able to wear flip-flops during the freezing winter, OR only be able to wear snow boots during the hottest summer?

Laugh Point_____ /1

Would you rather be able to experience the distant past OR see into the near future?

Laugh Point_____ /1

PASS THE BOOK TO PLAYER 2!

PLaYeR 2

(DON'T FORGET TO EXPLAIN YOUR ANSWERS!)

Would you rather be kissed by a camel wearing bright, red lipstick **OR** hugged by an alien wearing old lady perfume?

Laugh Point_____ /1

Would you rather freeze your tongue to a pole **OR** put icicles up your nose?

Laugh Point_____ /1

PLaYeR 2

Would you rather be stuck in an elevator with someone who has really bad gas for 6 hours, OR trapped on the roof of a skyscraper overnight?

Laugh Point_____ /1

Would you rather play golf with only one hand OR try archery, but have to wear high heels the whole time?

Laugh Point_____ /1

TIME TO SCORE YOUR POINTS! →

ADD UP ALL YOUR POINTS FROM ROUND 11.
THE PLAYER WITH THE MOST POINTS IS CROWNED
THE GROSS LAUGH MASTER!

PLAYER 1  /4

ROUND TOTAL

PLAYER 2  /4

ROUND TOTAL

_____

THE GROSS
LAUGH MASTER

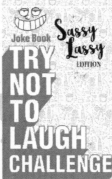

OTHER JOKE BOOKS!

 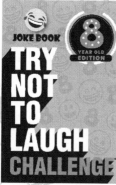 

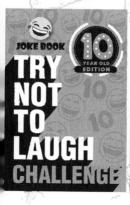 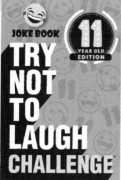 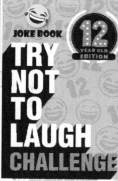

IF YOU HAVE ENJOYED OUR BOOK, WE WOULD LOVE FOR YOU TO REVIEW US ON AMAZON!

Made in the USA
Monee, IL
03 December 2020

50777053R00044